D0719638

© 1997 Geddes & Grosset Ltd
Published by Geddes & Grosset Ltd,
New Lanark, Scotland.

ISBN 1 85534 865 9

Produced by Simon Girling & Associates,
Hadleigh, Suffolk.

Printed and bound in China.

10 9 8 7 6 5 4 3 2 1

# Visit the
# Doctor

**GEDDES & GROSSET**

It was breakfast time. Mum was setting the table and Dad was making toast. Susie came into the kitchen.

"I'm hungry," she said. "What's for breakfast?"

"Boiled eggs and toast," said Dad.

"Where's Sam?" asked Mum.

"Sam says it's too cold to get up," said Susie. "I think that he is just being lazy. It's not cold today!"

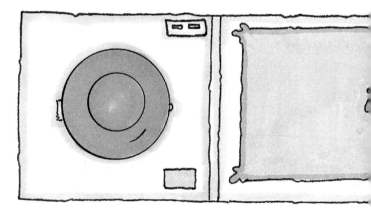

Mum went up to see Sam. He was still lying in bed and he was shivering.

"Come on, Sam," said Mum. "It's time to get up!"

"I can't get up," said Sam. "I'm cold and my throat hurts. I'm sore all over."

Mum felt Sam's forehead. It was hot.

"Oh dear, Sam. You have a fever," Mum said. "Open your mouth and say 'Aah'."

Sam opened his mouth and said "Aah," and Mum peered inside.

"Poor Sam. That *is* a sore throat! I had better take you to the doctor's. You stay in bed and keep warm. I shall phone to make an appointment."

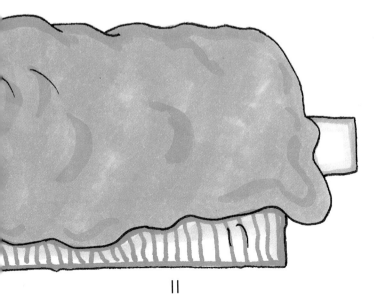

Mum went downstairs to telephone the doctor. Sam curled up tight under his covers, feeling sorry for himself.

"Is Sam ill?" asked Susie.

"Sam doesn't feel well at all," said Mum

13

After she had phoned the doctor, Mum went back to see Sam.

"We can see Dr Bell at nine o'clock," said Mum. "Put some warm clothes on and then I'll take you there in the car."

Dad came into the bedroom.

"I'm going to the doctor's," said Sam. "I don't want to go."

"Don't you worry," said Dad. "Dr Bell is a very nice man. He'll make you better."

A little while later, Mum, Susie and Sam were sitting in the doctor's waiting room. Sam was still looking miserable.

Dr Bell called them into his room. "What brings you here today, young man?" he said to Sam.

"My throat hurts," said Sam.

"Well, we can't have that!" said Dr Bell.

"Let's have a look."

Dr Bell got Sam to open his mouth and say "Aah", just as Mum had done. He shone his torch inside and had a good look at Sam's throat.

"Tonsillitis," he said. "Your throat must
be very sore indeed, Sam. I'll listen to
your chest and look in your ears to make
sure that they are all right. Would you like
to help?" he said to Susie.

Susie nodded.

"Righto" said Dr Bell. "You can be my assistant. He showed Susie how to listen to Sam's heartbeat and breathing with a stethoscope. He let Sam have a go too. Then he listened to Sam's chest himself. Then he looked inside Sam's ears with his auroscope.

"No problems there, Sam," said Dr Bell, "but you need some medicine for that poor throat. Don't worry," he added with a smile, "it doesn't taste too bad!"

He wrote a note on his prescription pad for Mum to take to the chemist.

"This tells the chemist which medicine to give you," said Dr Bell. "One spoonful, three times a day, until the bottle is empty! I know you don't feel hungry just now, but try to drink as much as you can. You will feel better soon. You have been a brave boy, Sam. And thank you, Susie, for being my assistant."

"Thank you very much, Dr Bell," said Mum as they all got up to go.

"My pleasure," said Dr Bell.

They stopped at the chemist's to get Sam's medicine on the way home. When they got home, Mum gave Sam his first spoonful.

"It tastes quite nice!" said Sam.

"Can I have a taste?" asked Susie.

"No, Susie" said Mum. "The medicine will only help Sam, because he is not well. Medicines can harm you if you do not use them properly. That is why we keep them locked up in the medicine cabinet, so that no one takes any by mistake."

Sam was very tired. Mum tucked him up in bed and gave him a drink. Then Susie sat on the end of Sam's bed and Mum read them both a story. When the story was finished. Sam's eyes were beginning to close.

"Dr Bell was nice," he said, sleepily.

"You were a good boy at the doctor's," said Mum, "and Susie was a very good girl. I am very proud of both of you."

"But when will I feel better?" asked Sam.

"You will probably feel a lot better tomorrow," said Mum, "and even better the day after that."

And she was right.

29